Level 5-2　Test 1—Test 20

嗨！你今天練習了嗎？

完成一回習題後，你可以在該回次的◯打勾並在_____填寫成績。

一起檢核英文實力吧！

(Level 6 (Test 1—Test 40) 請見下一頁喔)

Level 6   Test 1—Test 40

Level 5-2 Test 1

Score

Class: _____ No.: _____ Name: _____

I. 文意字彙 (50%)

_____ 1. When little Johnny saw his father carry a b____e, he knew his father was going to work.

_____ 2. The e____r walls of the apartment need washing.

_____ 3. The diligent student is e____ed to a full scholarship.

_____ 4. The country is ruled by a r____n government, not by a king.

_____ 5. The gardener t____med the tree with a pair of garden shears.

II. 文意選填 (請忽略大小寫) (50%)

(A) scope	(B) porch	(C) pastries	(D) directory	(E) masterpieces

_____ 1. Amelia is good at making _____, especially banana pie.

_____ 2. Let me look up her telephone number in the _____.

_____ 3. In the English class, we were asked to read several literary _____ of the 20th century.

_____ 4. The boy was sitting on the _____ of the house waiting for his father to return.

_____ 5. The boss gave the staff _____ for creativity.

Level 5-2 Test 2

Score

Class: _____ No.: _____ Name: _____

I. 文意字彙 (50%)

_____ 1. The boy took third place in the race and got a b____e medal.

_____ 2. When the girl said she was going to tell a story, all of the kids c____red around her.

_____ 3. A lot of fans s_____ed for tickets for the concert.

_____ 4. The speaker s_____ned up his suit before entering the conference room.

_____ 5. The couple had a f____s time at the Christmas party.

II. 文意選填 (請忽略大小寫) (50%)

(A) attic	(B) idiot	(C) resemblance	(D) patch up	(E) disapprove of

_____ 1. It is surprising that the two brothers bear little _____ to each other.

_____ 2. All the toys I played with in my childhood are stored in the _____ now.

_____ 3. You _____! Don't you know you are fooled?

_____ 4. After an angry argument, it seemed impossible for the couple to _____ their relationship.

_____ 5. I strongly _____ sex before marriage.

2

進階英文字彙力 4501～6000 習題本

Level 5-2 Test 3

Score

Class: _____ No.: _____ Name: _____

I. 文意字彙 (50%)

_____ 1. I take it for g_____ted that children should respect their parents.

_____ 2. You must get a p____t for your invention so that no one else can copy it without your permission.

_____ 3. After being scolded by his mom, Tom s_____med the door in her face.

_____ 4. The village's population is largely c____ed of factory workers.

_____ 5. All the students agree to n____e Susie as the student representative.

II. 文意選填 (請忽略大小寫) (50%)

(A) sphere	(B) illusion	(C) therapist	(D) meantime	(E) investigator

_____ 1. A(n) _____ is an idea that is untrue or mistaken.

_____ 2. A(n) _____ is responsible for carrying out investigations.

_____ 3. A(n) _____ is an object that is round in shape like a ball.

_____ 4. The lady is a speech _____, helping children who have difficulty in speaking properly.

_____ 5. Our plane will depart one hour from now, and in the _____ we can shop around in the duty free stores.

Level 5-2 Test 4

Score

Class: _____ No.: _____ Name: _____

I. 文意字彙 (50%)

_____ 1. The musician has been f____d by classical music since childhood.

_____ 2. The t____n fees of universities have been raised recently.

_____ 3. Two genuine paintings of Van Gogh were put up for a____n.

_____ 4. Sam's essay is full of i____y and sarcasm.

_____ 5. The burglar d____ted the alarm system and then broke into the house.

II. 文意選填 (請忽略大小寫) (50%)

| (A) slot | (B) envious | (C) pathetic | (D) corridor | (E) bureaucracy |

_____ 1. The two boys stopped fighting as the teacher suddenly appeared at the end of the _____.

_____ 2. I have to deal with the school's _____ if I want to change courses.

_____ 3. Having lost all his money in gambling, the man is now caught in a very _____ situation.

_____ 4. Many girls are _____ of Natalie's beautiful face and perfect figure.

_____ 5. Insert some coins into the _____, push the button and then you will get the drink.

Level 5-2 Test 5

Score

Class: _____ No.: _____ Name: _____

I. 文意字彙 (50%)

_____ 1. Don't i____e in self-pity. It's useless to feel sorry for yourself all the time.

_____ 2. The drunk man s_____hed the bottle into pieces.

_____ 3. This student did not s____t his essay on time.

_____ 4. During the air r____d, people stayed in the shelters.

_____ 5. The lady divorced her husband for his g____d for wealth.

II. 文意選填 (請忽略大小寫) (50%)

(A) tumor	(B) butcher	(C) journalism	(D) filter out	(E) deliberate on

_____ 1. My mom often buys meat from that _____ because the meat he sells is quite fresh.

_____ 2. You need a special device to _____ dirt in the water.

_____ 3. It took me a few days to _____ whether I should accept the job.

_____ 4. The doctor is performing an operation to remove a _____ from the patient's brain.

_____ 5. Elijah resolved to go into _____, hoping that he could thus raise public awareness of many important social issues.

Level 5-2 Test 6

Score

Class: _____　　No.: _____　　Name: _____

I. 文意字彙 (50%)

_____ 1. The spy c_____ed a plan to steal the file.

_____ 2. A d_____t is a person who has firm belief in democracy.

_____ 3. The movie was shown from the v_____t of a little boy.

_____ 4. The couple decided to move from the m_____n area to the suburbs to avoid the noise and busy traffic.

_____ 5. The school bell is ringing. Please r_____e your seats.

II. 文意選填 (請忽略大小寫) (50%)

(A) smog	(B) episode	(C) rallied	(D) grieved	(E) notified

_____ 1. The development of the Internet is an important _____ in the history of technology.

_____ 2. Mr. Cannon has _____ for his dead wife for years.

_____ 3. The old man had trouble breathing because of the terrible _____ in the city.

_____ 4. All the members must be _____ of any changes in the program.

_____ 5. Many people _____ to the support of the candidate.

Level 5-2 Test 7

Score

Class: _____ No.: _____ Name: _____

I. 文意字彙 (50%)

_____ 1. Following the doctor's advice, Susan uses a m_____l amount of salt in her food.

_____ 2. I prefer to g_____l sausages rather than steam them.

_____ 3. The suggested r_____l price of the lamp is $10 each, but if you buy a dozen, I can give you a wholesale price.

_____ 4. The dish was too sour. The cook probably added too much v_____r.

_____ 5. Peter decided to apply for the job because of the s_____l salary.

II. 文意選填 (請忽略大小寫) (50%)

(A) snatched	(B) counseled	(C) uncovered	(D) squad	(E) notion

_____ 1. My doctor _____ me to exercise regularly to relieve my pressure.

_____ 2. I have no _____ of what will be waiting for me behind the door.

_____ 3. Put your bag under the arm lest it be _____.

_____ 4. The building had been evacuated before the bomb _____ arrived.

_____ 5. A plot against the president was _____ by some FBI agents.

Level 5-2 Test 8

Score

Class: _____ No.: _____ Name: _____

I. 文意字彙 (50%)

_____ 1. The soldier stood e_____t when saluting the general.

_____ 2. You need to renew your v_____a before it expires.

_____ 3. More d_____y evidence was found to prove his fraud.

_____ 4. Make sure your meals contain all the n_____ts that are necessary for good health.

_____ 5. You must g_____p the rope tightly. It's the only thing that can save your life.

II. 文意選填 (請忽略大小寫) (50%)

(A) jury	(B) carnival	(C) squashed	(D) inherited	(E) condemned

_____ 1. During the _____, there was a big parade, and thousands of people danced in the streets.

_____ 2. The President _____ the terrorists for the bloody attack.

_____ 3. Sam's big eyes were _____ from his mother.

_____ 4. Finally the _____ decided that the accused was innocent.

_____ 5. The cake got _____ because I sat on it accidentally.

Level 5-2 Test 9

Score

Class: _____ No.: _____ Name: _____

I. 文意字彙 (50%)

_____ 1. Black is still the p____g color of formal evening wear.

_____ 2. The speaker r____ed on without noticing that most of the listeners had fallen asleep.

_____ 3. I have a c____n to make—I spilled your perfume when you were out.

_____ 4. "U____e the idiom, everybody. It is important," said the teacher.

_____ 5. Even a casual o____r can tell the dramatic improvement of the polluted river.

II. 文意選填 (請忽略大小寫) (50%)

(A) erupted	(B) vomited	(C) combat	(D) landlord	(E) banner

_____ 1. The workers demonstrated under the _____ of equal employment opportunities.

_____ 2. Since over 10,000 soldiers had died in _____, the general decided to retreat.

_____ 3. The _____ decided to lower our rent because we took good care of the apartment.

_____ 4. The boy was sick and _____ all he had eaten.

_____ 5. The situation turned chaotic after the fight _____ between the two rival gangs.

Level 5-2 Test 10

Score

Class: _____ No.: _____ Name: _____

I. 文意字彙 (50%)

_____ 1. The travel agent gave us a b____h of travel brochures.

_____ 2. Father has his problems to worry about, so don't bother him with such p____y matters.

_____ 3. I took the e____r to the third floor of the store.

_____ 4. The man was c____ed to a wheelchair after the car crash.

_____ 5. The lifeguards are s____sing the children swimming in the pool.

II. 文意選填 (請忽略大小寫) (50%)

(A) creek	(B) ridge	(C) deputy	(D) moaned	(E) injected

_____ 1. The _____ used to be so clear that we could see fish in it.

_____ 2. The boy _____ when he was told to turn off the TV and go to bed.

_____ 3. Pigeons are resting on the _____ of the roof.

_____ 4. George is the _____ while his boss is on a business trip.

_____ 5. The nurse _____ the baby with vaccines.

進階英文字彙力 4501～6000 習題本

Level 5-2 Test 11

Score

Class: _____ No.: _____ Name: _____

I. 文意字彙 (50%)

_____ 1. A l____r is responsible for making laws.

_____ 2. Judging from the woman's last name, we can tell she is

d____ded from a royal family.

_____ 3. Jimmy attended the summer s____n of the university.

_____ 4. The singer was c____ted with a bunch of questions on her

age when meeting the press.

_____ 5. My parents have been very busy and always have s____ks

of work to do.

II. 文意選填 (請忽略大小寫) (50%)

(A) operational	(B) mode	(C) profound	(D) rifle	(E) vow

_____ 1. You can play the video game in easy, normal or hard _____.

_____ 2. The hunter went hunting in the woods with a(n) _____.

_____ 3. Edith made a(n) _____ that someday she would start her own business.

_____ 4. Some _____ problems in the new computer system caused the factory to

close up for a week.

_____ 5. The emotional trauma of his childhood has a(n) _____ effect on his

personality.

Level 5-2 Test 12

Score

Class: _____ No.: _____ Name: _____

I. 文意字彙 (50%)

_____ 1. Pollution is a major h____d to wildlife.

_____ 2. Much to my d____r, the doctor confirmed that I had cancer.

_____ 3. The government officials didn't reach a c____s on building the power plant.

_____ 4. The merchant stores the products in the w____e before distributing them to retail stores.

_____ 5. It was found that the two policemen had been in l____e with the drug dealer for many years.

II. 文意選填 (請忽略大小寫) (50%)

(A) ethics	(B) unemployment	(C) prohibited	(D) ticked	(E) stains

_____ 1. Cheating customers is a violation of business _____.

_____ 2. The factory is going to shut down. More than 1,000 workers face _____.

_____ 3. To protect the endangered species of wild animals, hunting is strictly _____ in this mountainous area.

_____ 4. My mom can't get these coffee _____ out of the carpet.

_____ 5. I didn't sleep well because the clock _____ too noisily.

Level 5-2 Test 13

Class: _____ No.: _____ Name: _____

I. 文意字彙 (50%)

_____ 1. Our lives will be at s_____e if the war breaks out.

_____ 2. This is only a c_____e experiment, so the result may not be accurate.

_____ 3. My uncle has an o_____d where he grows oranges and bananas.

_____ 4. Citizens over 20 have the c_____l right to vote.

_____ 5. Don't just stand in the d_____y. Come and help me carry the tools to the front yard.

II. 文意選填 (請忽略大小寫) (50%)

| (A) projection | (B) shattered | (C) suspended | (D) unfolded | (E) innovation |

_____ 1. The explosion _____ all the windows of the houses near the area.

_____ 2. The man's driver's license was _____ for a year.

_____ 3. The sofa can be _____ to make a bed.

_____ 4. The _____ on the screen showed a skeleton of a prehistoric human.

_____ 5. The cellphone is a great _____ in the communication industry.

Level 5-2 Test 14

Score

Class: _____ No.: _____ Name: _____

I. 文意字彙 (50%)

_____ 1. My mother bought these bananas from a fruit s_____l in the market.

_____ 2. The man was sent to prison because he had committed the election f__w__d.

_____ 3. Gabriel didn't buy pizza d_____h; he made it by himself.

_____ 4. An arrogant person is p_____e to believe that he is superior to anyone else.

_____ 5. The politician's argument for economic growth struck a c_____d with many people in the country.

II. 文意選填 (請忽略大小寫) (50%)

(A) wary	(B) compact	(C) unlocked	(D) diagnosed	(E) exclaimed

_____ 1. Hank _____ that this was the most marvelous performance he'd ever seen.

_____ 2. Charlotte _____ the door of her car to let me get in.

_____ 3. Children should be taught to be _____ of strangers.

_____ 4. Brady would like to rent a(n) _____ car instead of a luxurious one.

_____ 5. Ellen was _____ as having heart disease.

Level 5-2 Test 15

Score

Class: _____ No.: _____ Name: _____

I. 文意字彙 (50%)

_____ 1. The ship f_____ted with lumber was bound for Kaohsiung.

_____ 2. Drinking alcohol could make you do many w_____d things that you normally wouldn't do.

_____ 3. It is the responsibility of the personnel department to r_____t new employees.

_____ 4. Computer technology is u_____ed every year. It's always improving.

_____ 5. The girl b_____hed when she noticed the handsome boy was looking at her.

II. 文意選填 (請忽略大小寫) (50%)

(A) propaganda	(B) hockey	(C) outfits	(D) chores	(E) torch

_____ 1. Kimberly is always dressed in smart business _____ when she goes to work.

_____ 2. My job is to do the administrative _____ of the office.

_____ 3. Bruno and I held a(n) _____ while going through the dark tunnel.

_____ 4. The girls play _____ on ice in winter.

_____ 5. The mass media should not make _____ for any specific political party.

Level 5-2 Test 16

Score

Class: _____ No.: _____ Name: _____

I. 文意字彙 (50%)

_____ 1. When the fire alarm went off, all the audience b_____ted for the exit.

_____ 2. It is not healthy to suppress one's feelings. Everyone should find a proper o_____t for his or her emotions.

_____ 3. Chest pain can be one of the s_____ms of a heart attack.

_____ 4. Because of the thunder, Alex's dog kept w_____ning outside last night.

_____ 5. I praised the kid for his performance on stage to boost his e_____o.

II. 文意選填 (請忽略大小寫) (50%)

| (A) lounge | (B) frontier | (C) exclusive | (D) diameter | (E) honorable |

_____ 1. The trunk of the tree is about ten foot in _____.

_____ 2. The swimming pool is _____ to the members of the club.

_____ 3. We agreed to meet at the student _____ after school.

_____ 4. Many people think teaching was a(n) _____ profession.

_____ 5. A(n) _____ is a border between two countries.

Level 5-2 Test 17

Score

Class: _____ No.: _____ Name: _____

I. 文意字彙 (50%)

_____ 1. With his mouth full, the boy m_____ed something that I couldn't hear clearly.

_____ 2. The kid s_____red at the thought of staying in such a dark room alone.

_____ 3. I tried in vain to i_____e myself into the new community.

_____ 4. The pretty lake was s_____ling in the sunlight.

_____ 5. It is said that the p_____es would attack the ships at sea and take away valuables.

II. 文意選填 (請忽略大小寫) (50%)

(A) tackle	(B) traitor	(C) utilize	(D) compensation	(E) wig

_____ 1. That man is a(n) _____ who sells secrets to the enemy.

_____ 2. People have learned to _____ solar power as a source of energy.

_____ 3. Mary wore a blonde _____ and dark glasses, trying to disguise herself.

_____ 4. The government carried out economic policies to _____ inflation.

_____ 5. The airline paid the passenger US$500 in _____ for her lost luggage.

Level 5-2 Test 18

Score

Class: _____ No.: _____ Name: _____

I. 文意字彙 (50%)

_____ 1. Vegetables and fruit are good for your d_____n.

_____ 2. That part of the country is just a w_____s. No one lives there.

_____ 3. The old temple has fallen into d_____y because of lack of care.

_____ 4. Our company tried to reduce the o_____d to stay in business.

_____ 5. John spent a night in the t_____t lounge at Gatwick Airport.

II. 文意選填 (請忽略大小寫) (50%)

(A) tangle	(B) variable	(C) municipal	(D) hostage	(E) exile

_____ 1. The politician criticized the government and was sent into _____.

_____ 2. My younger brother is studying in that _____ library.

_____ 3. People on that train were taken _____ by several terrorists.

_____ 4. The quality of this restaurant is _____. Sometimes you can enjoy a yummy meal, but sometimes the food is terrible.

_____ 5. I usually wake up in the morning with my hair in a(n) _____.

Level 5-2 Test 19

Score

Level 5-2

Class: _____ No.: _____ Name: _____

I. 文意字彙 (50%)

_____ 1. The boss e_____ts those workers who are young and naive.

_____ 2. Sam measured the d_____ns of the room before buying some new furniture.

_____ 3. The will s_____fied exactly who should receive the old man's fortune.

_____ 4. Greed t_____ted the judge to take bribes.

_____ 5. When the politician was asked about the bribery scandal, he just s_____ged his shoulders and said nothing.

II. 文意選填 (請忽略大小寫) (50%)

(A) masculine	(B) scar	(C) overwhelming	(D) boredom	(E) plural

_____ 1. The car accident left a(n) _____ on her right arm.

_____ 2. Deep voice and facial hair are _____ characteristics.

_____ 3. Mice is the _____ form of mouse.

_____ 4. Ann was homesick. She had a(n) _____ desire to return home.

_____ 5. Rita paced the floor out of sheer _____.

Level 5-2 Test 20

Score

Class: _____ No.: _____ Name: _____

I. 文意字彙 (50%)

_____ 1. Emma has been e____c about classical music since she was ten years old.

_____ 2. The delay of our flight added another c____n to our trip.

_____ 3. Dragons are m____l creatures. I don't believe they really exist.

_____ 4. The candidate said he would d____e himself to children's welfare.

_____ 5. Rather than drive my car, I like to take the s____e bus to the office.

II. 文意選填 (請忽略大小寫) (50%)

(A) myth	(B) massage	(C) treaty	(D) boundary	(E) civic

_____ 1. These high mountains mark the _____ between the two nations.

_____ 2. The story about mermaids is a _____.

_____ 3. A good _____ helps relieve both physical and emotional stress.

_____ 4. It is a _____ duty to keep the environment clean.

_____ 5. The president signed a peace _____ with that country.

Level 6 Test 1

Score

Class: _____ No.: _____ Name: _____

Level 6

I. 文意字彙 (50%)

_____ 1. To speak English well, you should learn to pronounce both vowels and c_____ts correctly.

_____ 2. Mrs. Simpson's c_____l necklace goes perfectly with her pink dress.

_____ 3. To our a_____e, the couple sitting in front of us kept talking loudly in the concert.

_____ 4. You can d_____h the hood from your coat if you don't need it.

_____ 5. The store sells a variety of m_____e. You can get almost everything you want there.

II. 文意選填 (請忽略大小寫) (50%)

(A) veil	(B) notorious	(C) hospitable	(D) courtyard	(E) broth

_____ 1. The soup made with _____ is more delicious than that with water.

_____ 2. The lady is very _____ to anyone who visits her.

_____ 3. A _____ is partly or completely enclosed by the walls of a building.

_____ 4. The city is _____ for its crimes and drugs.

_____ 5. The groom lifted the bride's _____ and kissed her.

Level 6 Test 2

Score

Class: _____ No.: _____ Name: _____

I. 文意字彙 (50%)

_____ 1. Sandra is taking a_____cs for her infected wound in the leg.

_____ 2. The medication can s_____e your sore throat.

_____ 3. Bill walked on c_____hes after the car accident.

_____ 4. The girl found a flock of ducks swimming u_____h the bridge.

_____ 5. My mother's eyes b_____ed with fury when she learned that I had cheated on the exam.

II. 文意選填 (請忽略大小寫) (50%)

(A) examiner	(B) comet	(C) cement	(D) versatile	(E) cumulative

_____ 1. Halley's _____ can be seen from the earth about every 76 years.

_____ 2. Tom's _____ teaching experience finally made him a distinguished teacher.

_____ 3. Emily is a(n) _____ actress. She is good at acting, singing, and writing plays.

_____ 4. _____ can be used to build houses.

_____ 5. The student became very nervous because the _____ looked serious.

Level 6 Test 3

Score

Class: _____ No.: _____ Name: _____

Level 6

I. 文意字彙 (50%)

_____ 1. Rita's memory of the tragic accident has l_____red on for over ten years.

_____ 2. To prevent the infectious disease from spreading, everyone should be aware of personal h_____e.

_____ 3. Losing both of her parents, the little girl was raised in an o_____e.

_____ 4. *The Boy Who Cried Wolf* is a famous f_____e that tells readers the importance of being honest.

_____ 5. The mother bear would do anything to protect her c_____bs.

II. 文意選填 (請忽略大小寫) (50%)

(A) applicable	(B) sorrowful	(C) bleach	(D) excerpt	(E) oath

_____ 1. Without using _____, it's impossible to get rid of the stain.

_____ 2. Remember you are now under _____. All you say must be the truth.

_____ 3. No rule is _____ to every situation. There is always an exception.

_____ 4. A(n) _____ from Joanne's speech will appear in today's newspapers.

_____ 5. What a(n) _____ sight it is to see a starving child begging on the street!

Level 6 Test 4

Score

Class: _____ No.: _____ Name: _____

I. 文意字彙 (50%)

_____ 1. The f____e of roses fills the beautiful garden.

_____ 2. A l____d is a type of reptile with four legs and a long tail.

_____ 3. My friend goes jogging every day to burn off e____s fat.

_____ 4. Some students took those easy courses just to a____e credits.

_____ 5. The politician was a____ted, and the police still didn't know who killed him.

II. 文意選填 (請忽略大小寫) (50%)

(A) outward	(B) offspring	(C) odor	(D) vitality	(E) reckless

_____ 1. My brother took a shower to get rid of his terrible body ____.

_____ 2. It was ____ of him to go mountain-climbing without checking the weather report first.

_____ 3. The eighty-year-old man is still full of ____. He participates in lots of activities.

_____ 4. Mr. Smith's property was divided among his ____.

_____ 5. Never judge people purely by ____ appearances.

Level 6 Test 5

Score

Class: _____ No.: _____ Name: _____

Level 6

I. 文意字彙 (50%)

_____ 1. The ugly chimney was a b____t on the landscape here.

_____ 2. My sister has worked as an a____e at a beauty salon for about three years to learn the craft of hairdressing.

_____ 3. It is a difficult task to c____e such a comprehensive dictionary.

_____ 4. It is cruel of you to say o____t that you don't love her anymore.

_____ 5. Mrs. Mitchell bought an o____l carpet as a souvenir of her trip to India.

II. 文意選填 (請忽略大小寫) (50%)

| (A) wardrobe | (B) longevity | (C) recreational | (D) spontaneous | (E) aboriginal |

_____ 1. Irene's speech was so _____ that words seemed to be flowing out of her mouth and touching the hearts of the audience.

_____ 2. Some government officials suggested that the land should be returned to the _____ people.

_____ 3. We wished Ken _____ on his birthday.

_____ 4. Hiking is a very good _____ activity.

_____ 5. The little boy hid himself in the _____ while playing hide-and-seek with the other kids.

Level 6 Test 6

Score

Class: _____ No.: _____ Name: _____

I. 文意字彙 (50%)

_____ 1. If you r____e the speech beforehand, you will not be so nervous when you are giving it.

_____ 2. What if an unstoppable spear meets an immovable shield? It is a well-known p____x.

_____ 3. The mother is d____red by anxiety because her little daughter is missing.

_____ 4. The minister has been in the s____t since the revelation of his sex scandal.

_____ 5. The father is rocking the cradle gently and singing a l____y to comfort his baby.

II. 文意選填 (請忽略大小寫) (50%)

| (A) champagne | (B) algebra | (C) weary | (D) solitary | (E) calligraphy |

_____ 1. _____ is a type of mathematics in which signs and letters are used to represent numbers.

_____ 2. The studying center is almost empty except for a(n) _____ figure.

_____ 3. Let's pop a bottle of _____ to celebrate our victory!

_____ 4. _____ is beautiful and artistic handwriting created with a special brush.

_____ 5. After finishing the marathon, all the runners look _____ but satisfied.

Level 6 Test 7

Score

Class: _____ No.: _____ Name: _____

Level 6

I. 文意字彙 (50%)

_____ 1. Anna's rosy c_____n indicates her good health.

_____ 2. It's hard for me to d_____e between male and female birds. They look very much alike.

_____ 3. Kevin's room was o_____ted with beautiful photos.

_____ 4. A b_____r of Arts degree takes three to four years of full-time study in Taiwan.

_____ 5. The woman has difficulty getting pregnant due to some f_____y problems.

II. 文意選填 (請忽略大小寫) (50%)

(A) peacock	(B) woodpecker	(C) captive	(D) anthem	(E) lush

_____ 1. A(n) _____ is a big bird; the male can spread out its tail feathers to show off the bright colors.

_____ 2. A(n) _____ uses its beak to make holes in tree trunks.

_____ 3. Before the competition began, they played the national _____ of the host country.

_____ 4. Sue stood by the window, looking at the _____ garden where hundreds of flowers were in full bloom.

_____ 5. Hundreds of people in the theater were held _____ by some terrorists.

Level 6 Test 8

Score

Class: _____ No.: _____ Name: _____

I. 文意字彙 (50%)

_____ 1. During the rainy season, the river usually o_____ws and floods the fields along the river bank.

_____ 2. The farmer only uses organic f_____r to enrich the soil of his farm.

_____ 3. The young girl used a lot of makeup to cover the p_____es on her face.

_____ 4. The secretary took d_____n from the manager and sent his messages to other departments.

_____ 5. Do you know how to c_____e the distance between the earth and the moon?

II. 文意選填 (請忽略大小寫) (50%)

(A) harness	(B) disastrous	(C) maiden	(D) bosom	(E) capsule

_____ 1. Cathy put a _____ on the horse and rode away.

_____ 2. If you don't read the safety instructions carefully, you may suffer _____ consequences.

_____ 3. The tragic incident of Titanic's sinking on her _____ voyage was made into a movie.

_____ 4. The baby fell asleep in her mother's warm _____.

_____ 5. Medicine is usually in the form of a pill, a tablet or a _____.

Level 6 Test 9

Score

Class: _____ No.: _____ Name: _____

I. 文意字彙 (50%)

_____ 1. The milk is f_____fied with vitamin E and calcium.

_____ 2. The p_____r bears are endangered largely as a result of global warming.

_____ 3. Harper didn't become a p_____t until she became aware of her country's difficult situation.

_____ 4. A d_____r rules a country with absolute power.

_____ 5. Some workers were made redundant and laid off because of the c_____n of the factory.

II. 文意選填 (請忽略大小寫) (50%)

(A) preventive　　(B) reproductions　　(C) captions　　(D) synonyms　　(E) majestic

_____ 1. Jimmy decorates his new house with _____ of famous paintings.

_____ 2. People must take _____ measures against the coming typhoon.

_____ 3. "Small" and "little" are _____.

_____ 4. Read the _____ under the picture and you'll know what it is about.

_____ 5. In the distance stand the _____ Alps, with snow-capped peaks shining in the sun.

Level 6

Level 6 Test 10

Score

Class: _____ No.: _____ Name: _____

I. 文意字彙 (50%)

_____ 1. Lisa often cooks h_____l food for her children, like chicken soup and brown rice.

_____ 2. The sunflower oil contains less c_____l and is better for our health.

_____ 3. Many animals do not breed well in c_____y after they are taken away from their natural habitat.

_____ 4. Silk and wool are not s_____c fibers.

_____ 5. These workers are d_____e. We decide to stop hiring them.

II. 文意選填 (請忽略大小寫) (50%)

(A) inquired	(B) cigar	(C) auditorium	(D) anchor	(E) dazzled

_____ 1. John was _____ by the strong sunlight and could hardly see anything.

_____ 2. Uncle Jack called me and _____ after my father's condition.

_____ 3. Listen to the captain, and then you'll know the time to cast _____.

_____ 4. After dinner, my grandfather lit a(n) _____, blowing smoke into the air.

_____ 5. The _____ can hold 40,000 people.

Level 6 Test 11

Score

Class: _____ No.: _____ Name: _____

I. 文意字彙 (50%)

_____ 1. It is not p____e to eat in the library.

_____ 2. The minister met with several European c____ts to discuss how to stabilize the region's economy.

_____ 3. Politicians should be a____e for the promises they make to the people.

_____ 4. The p____t won the Academy Award for Best Original Screenplay.

_____ 5. F____e is the traditional stories of a particular people or country.

II. 文意選填 (請忽略大小寫) (50%)

(A) retrieve	(B) dispense	(C) mingle	(D) boycott	(E) tenant

_____ 1. The machine allows us to _____ with a lot of labor.

_____ 2. The _____ intentionally trashed the house for ridiculous reasons.

_____ 3. The software can help _____ deleted or lost files.

_____ 4. People called for a _____ against the shop for it sold expired food.

_____ 5. When you go to a party, you should try to be sociable and _____ with others.

Level 6

Level 6 Test 12

Score

Class: _____ No.: _____ Name: _____

I. 文意字彙 (50%)

_____ 1. The worker is tightening the screw with a s_____r.

_____ 2. Rachel prefers to go swimming to r_____h herself in summer.

_____ 3. Nancy felt uncomfortable a_____d so many people.

_____ 4. The price is 80 dollars i_____e of tax.

_____ 5. Rita spent a lot of time with her friend. Friendship is i_____e to her.

II. 文意選填 (請忽略大小寫) (50%)

(A) coupons	(B) tentative	(C) robust	(D) concise	(E) abstractions

_____ 1. Sally saves all kinds of _____ so that she can buy things at lower prices.

_____ 2. John is almost 90 years old, but he remains _____.

_____ 3. Some people find philosophy hard to understand because they think it is full of _____.

_____ 4. The applicant gave the interviewer a(n) _____ smile and started to make her self-introduction.

_____ 5. Kevin's _____ explanation clarified all of our doubts.

Level 6 Test 13

Score

Class: _____ No.: _____ Name: _____

I. 文意字彙 (50%)

_____ 1. G____y speaking, the equator is an imaginary line that divides the earth into the northern and southern hemispheres.

_____ 2. Studies show that a c____e is intelligent and emotional enough to appreciate natural beauty.

_____ 3. The sales manager p____red on the reasons why the new product couldn't bring in the profits as expected.

_____ 4. After Jimmy graduated from high school, he attended a military a____y

_____ 5. It is not easy to c____e a 600-page novel into a 90-minute film.

II. 文意選填 (請忽略大小寫) (50%)

(A) servings	(B) carefree	(C) renowned	(D) compasses	(E) virgin

_____ 1. Although I am over 60 years old, I still remember my _____ childhood.

_____ 2. It is awful that there are only few _____ forests left in the world.

_____ 3. Without a pair of _____, I can't draw a perfect circle.

_____ 4. How many _____ of vegetables do you eat every day?

_____ 5. Stephen King, a _____ writer of horror fiction, has published more than fifty books.

Level 6 Test 14

Score

Class: _____ No.: _____ Name: _____

I. 文意字彙 (50%)

_____ 1. D____s is a disease in which someone has too much sugar in their blood.

_____ 2. G____y is mathematics concerning the study and measurement of lines, angles, and shapes.

_____ 3. Penny doesn't have the b____e to defend her ideas.

_____ 4. Ben and I saw the p____ws of several upcoming films in the movie theater.

_____ 5. S____n is the process of keeping places clean and hygienic.

II. 文意選填 (請忽略大小寫) (50%)

(A) cashier	(B) downward	(C) irritated	(D) intimidated	(E) breakdown

_____ 1. The economy is on a(n) _____ trend. It goes from bad to worse.

_____ 2. Larry suffered from a nervous _____ because of his heavy workload.

_____ 3. Don't get _____ by the number of competitors.

_____ 4. Jane is not suitable for the job as a(n) _____ because she is poor at calculation.

_____ 5. The teacher got a bit _____ by his foolish questions.

Level 6 Test 15

Score

Class: _____ No.: _____ Name: _____

Level 6

I. 文意字彙 (50%)

_____ 1. More and more parents show their d____f in the present educational reform.

_____ 2. Building a school in her hometown is Judy's l____g goal.

_____ 3. The famous s____r is thinking about the design of the statue.

_____ 4. It is a growing problem that more and more families collapse due to the b____p of marriage.

_____ 5. Luckily there were no c____ties in the bombing.

II. 文意選填 (請忽略大小寫) (50%)

(A) affectionate (B) congressman (C) credible (D) chairperson (E) climax

_____ 1. The _____ of the film is a car chase on the highway.

_____ 2. If something is _____, it deserves to be trusted.

_____ 3. A(n) _____ is a member of the U.S. Congress.

_____ 4. Whenever I call on my grandmother, she greets me with a(n) _____ hug.

_____ 5. The _____, the head of the organization, decides who can speak in today's meeting.

Level 6 Test 16

Score

Class: _____ No.: _____ Name: _____

I. 文意字彙 (50%)

_____ 1. We have to hire more people to l____n the increased workload.

_____ 2. Laziness is Jason's major f____w.

_____ 3. The a_____m of "polite" is "rude."

_____ 4. Many people like the s_____y of the design. They don't like complicated things.

_____ 5. Running out of fuel, the truck began to lose m_____m.

II. 文意選填 (請忽略大小寫) (50%)

(A) charitable	(B) jingle	(C) gleam	(D) conquest	(E) sociable

_____ 1. It looks like the World Cup will be the French team's next _____.

_____ 2. The orphanage is supported by _____ donations only.

_____ 3. Give it another try. There is still a _____ of hope.

_____ 4. Kids love to sing along with this advertising _____.

_____ 5. Serena was very _____. She enjoys meeting and talking to people.

進階英文字彙力 4501～6000 習題本

Level 6 Test 17

Score

Class: _____   No.: _____   Name: _____

I. 文意字彙 (50%)

_____ 1. People often buy new winter g_____ts for Chinese New Year.

_____ 2. They took d_____y action against several soldiers who violated the rule.

_____ 3. Three meetings were c_____med into Sophia's busy schedule.

_____ 4. Do you want to c_____e a person exactly the same as you?

_____ 5. We a_____ded Ian for having the courage to tell the truth.

II. 文意選填 (請忽略大小寫) (50%)

(A) distress	(B) brink	(C) joyous	(D) sloppy	(E) procession

_____ 1. According to the statistics, doctors' _____ handwriting killed more than 500 patients in the country per year.

_____ 2. The old man has lived in _____ since he lost his family in the fire.

_____ 3. A wedding _____ is passing along the street.

_____ 4. It is reported that the company is on the _____ of bankruptcy.

_____ 5. The little girl sang in a _____ voice.

Level 6

37

Level 6 Test 18

Score

Class: _____ No.: _____ Name: _____

I. 文意字彙 (50%)

_____ 1. It's everybody's duty to c____e natural resources.

_____ 2. Ben read the city tour b____e before he went on a trip there.

_____ 3. The book makes a d____e of the government's secret funds.

_____ 4. The company decides to give the employees a raise in salary to boost their m____e.

_____ 5. The population of the country a____es to one million.

II. 文意選填 (請忽略大小寫) (50%)

(A) cramp	(B) itchy	(C) marginal	(D) esteem	(E) disturbance

_____ 1. Ida doesn't like to wear woolen sweaters because they would make her feel _____.

_____ 2. Because of his contribution to the field of medicine, the scholar is held in high _____.

_____ 3. The runner didn't warm up beforehand and got a(n) _____ during the race.

_____ 4. The loud noise of the traffic causes a(n) _____ to people living along the streets.

_____ 5. The project is of _____ interest to the investors, and thus is bound to fail.

Level 6 Test 19

Score

Class: _____ No.: _____ Name: _____

I. 文意字彙 (50%)

_____ 1. The policy met with a h_____l of criticism. Many people complained about the inconvenience it had brought about.

_____ 2. Even though Bob transferred to his new school a week ago, he has made good a_____n to the new environment.

_____ 3. Don't d_____l on your past. It is no use thinking too much about it.

_____ 4. The task is a challenge for an expert, not to mention for a l_____n like me.

_____ 5. The huge c_____r was caused by the explosion.

II. 文意選填 (請忽略大小寫) (50%)

(A) discreet	(B) broil	(C) beautify	(D) spiral	(E) commonplace

_____ 1. Be careful when you walk down the _____ staircase.

_____ 2. Ophelia is a _____ person. She always plans everything down to the smallest detail.

_____ 3. Mr. Robinson used to _____ a fish as the main dish for dinner.

_____ 4. Our tour guide reminds us pickpocketing is _____ in this tourist attraction.

_____ 5. Do you agree that music can _____ your mind?

Level 6

Level 6 Test 20

Score

Class: _____ No.: _____ Name: _____

I. 文意字彙 (50%)

_____ 1. Everyone should be alert to this matter of great u_____y.

_____ 2. We don't want a l_____y explanation. Just try to briefly describe it in five minutes.

_____ 3. We tried to c_____e Vicky after she broke up with her boyfriend, but in vain.

_____ 4. People d_____e that woman for often stealing money from others.

_____ 5. Mom bought some pretty t_____es with different patterns on them to decorate the room.

II. 文意選填 (請忽略大小寫) (50%)

| (A) heroin | (B) notable | (C) analogy | (D) escort | (E) radiant |

_____ 1. The restaurant is _____ for its creamy tomato pasta.

_____ 2. The criminal was sent to jail under _____.

_____ 3. The drug dealer was caught selling _____ to the addict.

_____ 4. The speaker drew a(n) _____ between the two things and pointed out that they had many similar traits.

_____ 5. The girl with a(n) _____ smile was the center of attention.

Level 6 Test 21

Score

Class: _____ No.: _____ Name: _____

I. 文意字彙 (50%)

_____ 1. Julia ran out of her house in d____y when the big earthquake suddenly occurred.

_____ 2. It takes perseverance to accomplish such a f____e task.

_____ 3. Some people believe that certain herbs can help p____y the blood.

_____ 4. An emperor has absolute s____y over his people. Everyone has to listen to him.

_____ 5. Some students fell asleep during the long and t____e speech.

II. 文意選填 (請忽略大小寫) (50%)

| (A) violinist | (B) perishable | (C) isle | (D) indignant | (E) shabby |

_____ 1. We spent our vacation on a tropical _____.

_____ 2. Tina was _____ about being discriminated by her colleagues and called them racists.

_____ 3. Milk and meat are _____ foods so you should store them in the refrigerator.

_____ 4. A beggar in _____ clothes begged for money on the street.

_____ 5. The performance of the _____ in the concert was very impressive.

Level 6 Test 22

Score

Class: _____ No.: _____ Name: _____

I. 文意字彙 (50%)

_____ 1. The essence e_____ted from the rare plants is very expensive.

_____ 2. The politician f_____ed his opinions on the controversial issue during the debate.

_____ 3. Tony had badly hurt his knee and was l_____ping painfully.

_____ 4. The couple moved to the o_____s of the city to avoid the noise of the traffic.

_____ 5. Betty r_____med the streets looking for interesting shops.

II. 文意選填 (請忽略大小寫) (50%)

(A) persevering	(B) shaver	(C) superstitious	(D) disposable	(E) electrician

_____ 1. The _____ is busy repairing the electric motor.

_____ 2. These plastic spoons are _____. However, I think we should use them again.

_____ 3. Sam uses a(n) _____ to shave his beard every morning.

_____ 4. Laura is very _____ and won't go out without bringing her lucky coin.

_____ 5. As long as you are _____, you can achieve your goal one day.

Level 6 Test 23

Score

Class: _____ No.: _____ Name: _____

Level 6

I. 文意字彙 (50%)

_____ 1. The riot was soon s_____sed by the police.

_____ 2. The rain came down in t_____ts and caused a flood.

_____ 3. Many people around the world m_____ned for Mother Teresa's death.

_____ 4. Nelson was e_____ed to general manager because of his excellent performance and management ability.

_____ 5. When my grandfather had an operation, all of my family worked in r_____ys to take care of him.

II. 文意選填 (請忽略大小寫) (50%)

(A) stepfather	(B) janitor	(C) persistence	(D) vocational	(E) hoarse

_____ 1. Carol's _____ paid off when her company finally promoted her.

_____ 2. Kevin is my mother's second husband, which means he is my _____ in the family.

_____ 3. My neighbor used to be a _____ looking after a large office building in the city.

_____ 4. The little boy's voice became _____ because he had been shouting all day.

_____ 5. Helen studies in a _____ school, learning the skills at cooking.

Level 6 Test 24

Score

Class: _____ No.: _____ Name: _____

I. 文意字彙 (50%)

_____ 1. My mother prefers j____e tea to oolong tea.

_____ 2. Shelly o____d their scheme for robbing a bank.

_____ 3. You should d____e of batteries carefully, or they might pollute the environment.

_____ 4. Karen fluttered her e____hes at me and gave me a charming smile.

_____ 5. Daniel's impressive q____ns have won him many job interviews.

II. 文意選填 (請忽略大小寫) (50%)

(A) maple	(B) reliance	(C) forthcoming	(D) mournful	(E) surge

_____ 1. Don't place too much _____ on your instinct. Think rationally before taking actions.

_____ 2. The leaves of _____ trees turn red in autumn.

_____ 3. A series of activities will take place in the _____ week.

_____ 4. Abby felt a _____ of jealousy when her boyfriend praised another girl.

_____ 5. The _____ howl of the stray dog made me decide to adopt it.

Level 6 Test 25

Score

Class: _____ No.: _____ Name: _____

I. 文意字彙 (50%)

_____ 1. Tim m_____ws the lawns for his neighbors to earn some pocket money.

_____ 2. Mom cut the cabbage into long s_____ds to make salad.

_____ 3. Seeing its master, the puppy w_____ged its tail excitedly.

_____ 4. The manager's reputation was m_____red by the scandal.

_____ 5. The attendant u_____red me along the aisle to my seat.

II. 文意選填 (請忽略大小寫) (50%)

| (A) overlapping | (B) grapefruit | (C) honorary | (D) injustice | (E) rubbish |

_____ 1. A heap of _____ around the street corner attracted a lot of flies.

_____ 2. The writer received a(n) _____ degree from York University.

_____ 3. Our jobs are _____. When there is a mistake, it is hard to decide who is to blame.

_____ 4. We ordered a cup of coffee and a glass of _____ juice without ice.

_____ 5. African Americans have combated _____ for hundreds of years.

Level 6

進階英文字彙力 4501～6000 習題本

Level 6 Test 26

Score

Class: _____ No.: _____ Name: _____

I. 文意字彙 (50%)

_____ 1. The tires are easily worn down if you often drive on r_____d ground.

_____ 2. The team decided to build a refuge for s_____y dogs.

_____ 3. The climber f_____ed her left arm after falling over a slippery rock.

_____ 4. The patient is recovering from a heart t_____t operation.

_____ 5. We need more kitchen u_____ls to cook a feast for fifty people.

II. 文意選填 (請忽略大小寫) (50%)

| (A) radish | (B) solitude | (C) factions | (D) walnuts | (E) distraction |

_____ 1. A _____ is a red vegetable that is often eaten raw and has a spicy taste.

_____ 2. I enjoy the moments of _____ before a busy day begins.

_____ 3. The ingredients of this apple pie include apples, _____, flour, and butter.

_____ 4. The teacher was driven to _____ by the mischievous students.

_____ 5. The party split into two _____ due to different political views.

Level 6 Test 27

Score

Class: _____ No.: _____ Name: _____

I. 文意字彙 (50%)

_____ 1. I have tried i_____e times to contact the reporter.

_____ 2. The hole in the o_____e layer was caused by pollution.

_____ 3. My brother u_____red a groan when I told him to dump the garbage.

_____ 4. There has been a r_____h of robberies in the neighborhood recently.

_____ 5. I fell off my bike yesterday, because a dog suddenly g_____led at me.

II. 文意選填 (請忽略大小寫) (50%)

(A) ward	(B) prestige	(C) mediator	(D) mustache	(E) pickpocket

_____ 1. My sister is good at negotiation and has the qualities to be a _____.

_____ 2. There is keen competition among students who wish to enter a university of high _____.

_____ 3. I think the actor looks more mature and charming with a _____ on his upper lip.

_____ 4. The _____ was under arrest because he was caught stealing a tourist's wallet.

_____ 5. Please keep your voice down for there are other patients in the same _____.

Level 6

Level 6 Test 28

Score

Class: _____ No.: _____ Name: _____

I. 文意字彙 (50%)

_____ 1. Stop g_____ling about your job. I don't think you can find a job better than this one.

_____ 2. The coffee tasted bitter, so Bob asked the waiter to bring him a p_____t of sugar.

_____ 3. The magician's performance is s_____g. I am impressed by it.

_____ 4. The v_____e will be given to medical and nursing staff in the hospital first.

_____ 5. Oliver tends to stay at h_____ls instead of luxurious hotels while traveling abroad.

II. 文意選填 (請忽略大小寫) (50%)

| (A) trifles | (B) lockers | (C) reptiles | (D) pilgrim | (E) endurance |

_____ 1. Snakes and lizards are _____.

_____ 2. Don't waste your time on _____. You should work on more important things.

_____ 3. Swimming across the strait requires great _____.

_____ 4. We keep our clothes and bags in the _____ when we go swimming in the pool.

_____ 5. A(n) _____ is a person who travels, usually over a long distance, for a religious purpose.

Level 6 Test 29

Score

Class: _____ No.: _____ Name: _____

I. 文意字彙 (50%)

_____ 1. Mom closed the s_____rs to keep out the strong sunlight.

_____ 2. Driven by v_____y, my cousin bought that sports car.

_____ 3. What can we do to e_____e the company's reputation?

_____ 4. I was deep in m_____n when the phone rang.

_____ 5. When the driver saw another car coming straight toward him,

his i_____e reaction was to turn to the right side.

II. 文意選填 (請忽略大小寫) (50%)

(A) lodging	(B) nagging	(C) hovering	(D) warranty	(E) stutter

_____ 1. A hawk is _____ over the dying deer.

_____ 2. The school dormitory charges high for board and _____.

_____ 3. I have a bad cold, and the _____ cough keeps me from sleeping well.

_____ 4. The student was so nervous that he replied with a _____.

_____ 5. This laptop computer comes with a year's _____.

Level 6

Level 6 Test 30

Score

Class: _____ No.: _____ Name: _____

I. 文意字彙 (50%)

_____ 1. Knowing that my uncle is always late, I don't r_____n on his arriving on time today.

_____ 2. I felt h_____d when my classmate called me a good-for-nothing in public.

_____ 3. This power generator is p_____led by water.

_____ 4. We s_____e with the earthquake victims.

_____ 5. A d_____y is a large building at college or university where students live.

II. 文意選填 (請忽略大小寫) (50%)

⒜ feasible	⒝ ordeal	⒞ savage	⒟ vapor	⒠ waterproof

_____ 1. The poor little girl was attacked by a(n) _____ dog.

_____ 2. When water boils, it turns to _____.

_____ 3. I don't think this plan is _____. It costs too much money to put the plan into practice.

_____ 4. The boy stayed calm throughout the _____ of being kidnapped and tried to find a way to escape.

_____ 5. My coat is _____ so I can wear it outdoors in rainy days.

Level 6 Test 31

Score

Class: _____ No.: _____ Name: _____

I. 文意字彙 (50%)

_____ 1. The patient grew too f_____e to say anything.

_____ 2. Car exhaust f_____es cause heavy air pollution in big cities.

_____ 3. Don't h_____h your back. Stand up straight!

_____ 4. Anyone who violates the law will be p_____ed.

_____ 5. If you go to bed early, you won't d_____e off all the time.

II. 文意選填 (請忽略大小寫) (50%)

(A) velvet	(B) logo	(C) mentality	(D) scraped	(E) paralyzed

_____ 1. The _____ of McDonald's two arches in bright yellow has become world-famous.

_____ 2. The driver _____ the snow off the car windows.

_____ 3. That man has the get-rich-quick _____ and doesn't know the value of hard work.

_____ 4. The car accident _____ traffic on the freeway.

_____ 5. You look pretty in black _____.

Level 6

進階英文字彙力 4501～6000 習題本

Level 6 Test 32

Score

Class: _____ No.: _____ Name: _____

I. 文意字彙 (50%)

_____ 1. Don't e_____e the mistake with failure. If you fix it in time, you still can succeed.

_____ 2. The boy spoke in a high, f_____e voice, imitating his sister.

_____ 3. We need an o_____r to make arrangements for the party.

_____ 4. A car crashed into another at the i_____n of the two main roads.

_____ 5. The tennis player, who always accepts victory or defeat graciously, has won praise for his good s_____p.

II. 文意選填 (請忽略大小寫) (50%)

| (A) tucked | (B) skimmed | (C) subscribed | (D) mermaid | (E) veterinarian |

_____ 1. A _____ is a legendary creature with a woman's upper body and a fish's tail.

_____ 2. Sam _____ his shirt into his trousers.

_____ 3. A _____ is a person who is skilled in treating animal diseases and injuries.

_____ 4. The professor _____ the pages to find the main ideas in the report.

_____ 5. I _____ to several magazines, and it cost me a lot of money.

進階英文字彙力 4501～6000 習題本

Level 6 Test 33

Score

Class: _____ No.: _____ Name: _____

I. 文意字彙 (50%)

_____ 1. The boat struck a r____f and began to sink.

_____ 2. When I scolded my son, he shouted back and made a sharp
r____t.

_____ 3. Judy went to Paris on the s____r of the moment. She didn't
plan it beforehand.

_____ 4. All the students were e____ed from their classrooms
because of an earthquake.

_____ 5. The teacher h____ned his heart when dealing with his
naughty boy students.

II. 文意選填 (請忽略大小寫) (50%)

(A) tan	(B) turmoil	(C) hypocrite	(D) migrants	(E) latitudes

_____ 1. The plant can only be found at high ____. It doesn't grow in warm
weather.

_____ 2. There are a lot of ____ looking for jobs in this big city.

_____ 3. I got a ____ after my vacation at the beach.

_____ 4. My mind was in such a ____ that I didn't know what I was saying.

_____ 5. That man is such a ____ that he praises his girlfriend to her face but
speaks ill of her behind her back.

Level 6

53

Level 6 Test 34

Score

Class: _____ No.: _____ Name: _____

I. 文意字彙 (50%)

_____ 1. Which d_____g would you like? Caesar, Italian, or Thousand Island?

_____ 2. A fish moves and keeps its balance with its f_____ns.

_____ 3. Calm down. Why are you making such a f_____s about that?

_____ 4. An i_____g is a huge mass of frozen ice in the sea.

_____ 5. The windows v_____ed when a strong wind blew.

II. 文意選填 (請忽略大小寫) (50%)

| (A) lotion | (B) twilight | (C) succession | (D) wholesome | (E) miscellaneous |

_____ 1. At the garage sale, you can find _____ used household items sold at very low prices.

_____ 2. What you need is fresh, healthy, and _____ food.

_____ 3. A _____ of defeats discouraged the athlete from moving forward.

_____ 4. The professor devoted his _____ years to the education of the deaf.

_____ 5. This _____ keeps the moisture of your skin and makes you look young.

Level 6 Test 35

Score

Class: _____ No.: _____ Name: _____

Level 6

I. 文意字彙 (50%)

_____ 1. Mary's neighbor became a w____w after her husband died 10 years ago.

_____ 2. My aunt has d____l citizenship. She holds an American and a Japanese passports at the same time.

_____ 3. We mustn't waste our f____e resources. We should make the most of them.

_____ 4. There are many stars t____ling in the sky at night.

_____ 5. The old man fainted and s____ped to the floor.

II. 文意選填 (請忽略大小寫) (50%)

(A) outing	(B) lottery	(C) stagger	(D) novice	(E) intonation

_____ 1. The man spent his last pennies on a(n) _____ ticket, hoping to win a big prize.

_____ 2. I am a(n) _____ at gardening. Would you please give me some advice on what to do with these flowers?

_____ 3. The drunk walked with a(n) _____ and accidentally fell off the bridge.

_____ 4. My family enjoyed the _____ at the beach last weekend.

_____ 5. In many languages, a rising _____ usually means a question.

Level 6 Test 36

Score

Class: _____ No.: _____ Name: _____

I. 文意字彙 (50%)

_____ 1. We decide to m____e our kitchen and have a dishwasher installed.

_____ 2. The girl's parents told her not to open the box, but she could not help taking a p____k inside.

_____ 3. The gas s____ed the victims who were trapped in the house. Many of them fainted.

_____ 4. My classmate e____ls not only in Chinese but also in English.

_____ 5. Two g____rs robbed the bank.

II. 文意選填 (請忽略大小寫) (50%)

(A) outlaw	(B) tempo	(C) posture	(D) dubious	(E) implicit

_____ 1. The fast _____ of city life exhausted me.

_____ 2. We were _____ about the drug's effects claimed by its producer.

_____ 3. Christians have _____ faith in God.

_____ 4. Robin Hood was no ordinary _____.

_____ 5. Lucy, a couch potato, enjoys sitting in a relaxed _____ and watching TV.

Level 6 Test 37

Score

Class: _____   No.: _____   Name: _____

I. 文意字彙 (50%)

_____ 1. A lot of vegetarians feel that it's r____g to eat meat.

_____ 2. Ted hated others to i____e on his private affairs.

_____ 3. The o____k for the new product is still uncertain. We are not sure yet whether it will sell well.

_____ 4. The flight attendant was arrested for s____ling drugs.

_____ 5. Due to the drought, thousands of people died of s____n in Africa.

II. 文意選填 (請忽略大小寫) (50%)

(A) revolt	(B) suitcase	(C) monarch	(D) duration	(E) loudspeaker

_____ 1. The people wanted to overthrow the _____ and establish a democratic government.

_____ 2. It always takes me a long time to pack a _____ before a trip.

_____ 3. When you are addressing a large audience, you may need a _____ to make yourself heard.

_____ 4. There will be no more flights for the _____ of the typhoon.

_____ 5. Many people in the country rose in _____ against the cruel ruler.

Level 6 Test 38

Score

Class: _____ No.: _____ Name: _____

I. 文意字彙 (50%)

_____ 1. The farmer begins his work at dawn and returns home at
d___k.

_____ 2. The candidate had his campaign highly p_____ed so that
more voters would pay attention to his policy.

_____ 3. I will e____t myself to achieve my goal.

_____ 4. Never u___e your opponent. I don't think you can defeat
him easily.

_____ 5. The medicine can help l_____n the pain in your leg.

II. 文意選填 (請忽略大小寫) (50%)

(A) sneakers   (B) hemispheres   (C) refreshments   (D) nurturing   (E) flourishing

_____ 1. If your business is _____, it is successful and prosperous.

_____ 2. The brain is divided into the left and right _____.

_____ 3. We believe both parents and schools should be responsible for _____
children's interests.

_____ 4. After two hours in the meeting, we took a short break and had some
_____.

_____ 5. I gave my boyfriend a pair of black _____ as his birthday gift.

Level 6 Test 39

Class: _____ No.: _____ Name: _____

I. 文意字彙 (50%)

_____ 1. To set a good example for students, teachers should practice what they p____h.

_____ 2. The little girl p____fed out her cheeks and blew air into the balloon.

_____ 3. My cousin f____ked out of high school for failing too many academic subjects.

_____ 4. Luckily, I only suffered s____l injuries in that nasty accident.

_____ 5. Tom's h____c deeds have become legends, well-known to the town folks.

II. 文意選填 (請忽略大小寫) (50%)

(A) vines	(B) oases	(C) tilted	(D) refuted	(E) wrinkled

_____ 1. There are some _____ in the desert where travelers can get some water.

_____ 2. The suspect _____ the accusations against him.

_____ 3. The shirt _____ when Ms. Bond took it out of the wardrobe.

_____ 4. The cute puppy _____ its head to one side, looking at us.

_____ 5. The wall is covered with grape _____.

Level 6 Test 40

Score

Class: _____ No.: _____ Name: _____

I. 文意字彙 (50%)

_____ 1. The photographer z_____med in on the model's face to take
a picture.

_____ 2. I couldn't sleep well last night because someone s_____ed
very loudly in the next room.

_____ 3. Tell me the e_____n date on your membership card.

_____ 4. I walked on t_____e to avoid making any noise.

_____ 5. My father is always p_____l for work; he is never late.

II. 文意選填 (請忽略大小寫) (50%)

| (A) madam | (B) oatmeal | (C) setback | (D) gloom | (E) motherhood |

_____ 1. There has been a sense of _____ in the family since their pet was gone.

_____ 2. Before you decide to have a baby, make sure that you are ready for
_____.

_____ 3. The politician suffered a(n) _____ in his political career and decided to
give up his post.

_____ 4. May I bring you something to drink, _____?

_____ 5. Helen can make very delicious _____ cookies.

進階英文字彙力
4501～6000
習題本

Answer Key

Level 5–2 Test 1
I. 1. briefcase 2. exterior 3. entitled
   4. republican 5. trimmed
II. 1. C 2. D 3. E 4. B 5. A

Level 5–2 Test 2
I. 1. bronze 2. clustered 3. scrambled
   4. straightened 5. fabulous
II. 1. C 2. A 3. B 4. D 5. E

Level 5–2 Test 3
I. 1. granted 2. patent 3. slammed
   4. comprised 5. nominate
II. 1. B 2. E 3. A 4. C 5. D

Level 5–2 Test 4
I. 1. fascinated 2. tuition 3. auction
   4. irony 5. disconnected
II. 1. D 2. E 3. C 4. B 5. A

Level 5–2 Test 5
I. 1. indulge 2. smashed 3. submit
   4. raid 5. greed
II. 1. B 2. D 3. E 4. A 5. C

Level 5–2 Test 6
I. 1. conceived 2. democrat 3. viewpoint
   4. metropolitan 5. resume
II. 1. B 2. D 3. A 4. E 5. C

Level 5–2 Test 7
I. 1. minimal 2. grill 3. retail 4. vinegar
   5. substantial
II. 1. B 2. E 3. A 4. D 5. C

Level 5–2 Test 8
I. 1. erect 2. visa 3. documentary
   4. nutrients 5. grip
II. 1. B 2. E 3. D 4. A 5. C

Level 5–2 Test 9
I. 1. prevailing 2. rattled 3. confession
   4. Underline 5. observer
II. 1. E 2. C 3. D 4. B 5. A

Level 5–2 Test 10
I. 1. batch 2. petty 3. escalator
   4. confined 5. supervising
II. 1. A 2. D 3. B 4. C 5. E

Level 5–2 Test 11
I. 1. lawmaker 2. descended 3. session
   4. confronted 5. stacks
II. 1. B 2. D 3. E 4. A 5. C

Level 5–2 Test 12
I. 1. hazard 2. despair 3. consensus
   4. warehouse 5. league
II. 1. A 2. B 3. C 4. E 5. D

Level 5–2 Test 13
I. 1. stake 2. crude 3. orchard
   4. constitutional 5. doorway
II. 1. B 2. C 3. D 4. A 5. E

Level 5–2 Test 14
I. 1. stall 2. fraud 3. dough 4. prone
   5. chord
II. 1. E 2. C 3. A 4. B 5. D

Level 5–2 Test 15
I. 1. freighted 2. weird 3. recruit
   4. upgraded 5. blushed
II. 1. C 2. D 3. E 4. B 5. A

Level 5–2 Test 16
I. 1. bolted 2. outlet 3. symptoms
   4. whining 5. ego
II. 1. D 2. C 3. A 4. E 5. B

Level 5–2 Test 17
I. 1. mumbled 2. shivered 3. integrate
   4. sparkling 5. pirates
II. 1. B 2. C 3. E 4. A 5. D

Level 5–2 Test 18
I. 1. digestion 2. wilderness 3. decay
   4. overhead 5. transit
II. 1. E 2. C 3. D 4. B 5. A

Level 5–2 Test 19
I. 1. exploits 2. dimensions 3. specified
   4. tempted 5. shrugged
II. 1. B 2. A 3. E 4. C 5. D

Level 5–2 Test 20
I. 1. enthusiastic 2. complication
   3. mythical 4. dedicate 5. shuttle
II. 1. D 2. A 3. B 4. E 5. C

Level 6 Test 1

I. 1. consonants   2. coral   3. annoyance
   4. detach   5. merchandise
II. 1. E   2. C   3. D   4. B   5. A

Level 6 Test 2

I. 1. antibiotics   2. soothe   3. crutches
   4. underneath   5. blazed
II. 1. B   2. E   3. D   4. C   5. A

Level 6 Test 3

I. 1. lingered   2. hygiene   3. orphanage
   4. fable   5. cubs
II. 1. C   2. E   3. A   4. D   5. B

Level 6 Test 4

I. 1. fragrance   2. lizard   3. excess
   4. accumulate   5. assassinated
II. 1. C   2. E   3. D   4. B   5. A

Level 6 Test 5

I. 1. blot   2. apprentice   3. compile
   4. outright   5. oriental
II. 1. D   2. E   3. B   4. C   5. A

Level 6 Test 6

I. 1. rehearse   2. paradox   3. devoured
   4. spotlight   5. lullaby
II. 1. B   2. D   3. A   4. E   5. C

Level 6 Test 7

I. 1. complexion   2. differentiate
   3. ornamented   4. bachelor   5. fertility
II. 1. A   2. B   3. D   4. E   5. C

Level 6 Test 8

I. 1. overflows   2. fertilizer   3. pimples
   4. dictation   5. compute
II. 1. A   2. B   3. C   4. D   5. E

Level 6 Test 9

I. 1. fortified   2. polar   3. patriot
   4. dictator   5. computerization
II. 1. B   2. A   3. D   4. C   5. E

Level 6 Test 10

I. 1. healthful   2. cholesterol   3. captivity
   4. synthetic   5. dispensable
II. 1. E   2. A   3. D   4. B   5. C

Level 6 Test 11

I. 1. permissible   2. counterparts
   3. accountable   4. playwright   5. Folklore
II. 1. B   2. E   3. A   4. D   5. C

Level 6 Test 12

I. 1. screwdriver   2. refresh   3. amid
   4. inclusive   5. invaluable
II. 1. A   2. C   3. E   4. B   5. D

Level 6 Test 13

I. 1. Geographically   2. chimpanzee
   3. pondered   4. academy   5. condense
II. 1. B   2. E   3. D   4. A   5. C

Level 6 Test 14

I. 1. Diabetes   2. Geometry   3. backbone
   4. previews   5. Sanitation
II. 1. B   2. E   3. D   4. A   5. C

Level 6 Test 15

I. 1. disbelief   2. lifelong   3. sculptor
   4. breakup   5. casualties
II. 1. E   2. C   3. B   4. A   5. D

Level 6 Test 16

I. 1. lighten   2. flaw   3. antonym
   4. simplicity   5. momentum
II. 1. D   2. A   3. C   4. B   5. E

Level 6 Test 17

I. 1. garments   2. disciplinary   3. crammed
   4. clone   5. applauded
II. 1. D   2. A   3. E   4. B   5. C

Level 6 Test 18

I. 1. conserve   2. brochure   3. disclosure
   4. morale   5. approximates
II. 1. B   2. D   3. A   4. E   5. C

Level 6 Test 19

I. 1. hail   2. adaptation   3. dwell
   4. layman   5. crater
II. 1. D   2. A   3. B   4. E   5. C

Level 6 Test 20

I. 1. urgency   2. lengthy   3. console
   4. despise   5. textiles
II. 1. B   2. D   3. A   4. C   5. E

Level 6 Test 21
I. 1. dismay 2. formidable 3. purify
   4. superiority 5. tiresome
II. 1. C 2. D 3. B 4. E 5. A

Level 6 Test 22
I. 1. extracted 2. formulated 3. limping
   4. outskirts 5. roamed
II. 1. E 2. D 3. B 4. C 5. A

Level 6 Test 23
I. 1. suppressed 2. torrents 3. mourned
   4. elevated 5. relays
II. 1. C 2. A 3. B 4. E 5. D

Level 6 Test 24
I. 1. jasmine 2. overheard 3. dispose
   4. eyelashes 5. qualifications
II. 1. B 2. A 3. C 4. E 5. D

Level 6 Test 25
I. 1. mows 2. shreds 3. wagged
   4. marred 5. ushered
II. 1. E 2. C 3. A 4. B 5. D

Level 6 Test 26
I. 1. rugged 2. stray 3. fractured
   4. transplant 5. utensils
II. 1. A 2. B 3. D 4. E 5. C

Level 6 Test 27
I. 1. innumerable 2. ozone 3. uttered
   4. rash 5. growled
II. 1. C 2. B 3. D 4. E 5. A

Level 6 Test 28
I. 1. grumbling 2. packet 3. stunning
   4. vaccine 5. hostels
II. 1. C 2. A 3. E 4. B 5. D

Level 6 Test 29
I. 1. shutters 2. vanity 3. enhance
   4. meditation 5. instinctive
II. 1. C 2. A 3. B 4. E 5. D

Level 6 Test 30
I. 1. reckon 2. humiliated 3. propelled
   4. sympathize 5. dormitory
II. 1. C 2. D 3. A 4. B 5. E

Level 6 Test 31
I. 1. feeble 2. fumes 3. hunch
   4. prosecuted 5. doze
II. 1. B 2. D 3. C 4. E 5. A

Level 6 Test 32
I. 1. equate 2. feminine 3. organizer
   4. intersection 5. sportsmanship
II. 1. D 2. A 3. E 4. B 5. C

Level 6 Test 33
I. 1. reef 2. retort 3. spur 4. evacuated
   5. hardened
II. 1. E 2. D 3. A 4. B 5. C

Level 6 Test 34
I. 1. dressing 2. fins 3. fuss 4. iceberg
   5. vibrated
II. 1. E 2. D 3. C 4. B 5. A

Level 6 Test 35
I. 1. widow 2. dual 3. finite 4. twinkling
   5. slumped
II. 1. B 2. D 3. C 4. A 5. E

Level 6 Test 36
I. 1. modernize 2. peek 3. suffocated
   4. excels 5. gangsters
II. 1. B 2. D 3. E 4. A 5. C

Level 6 Test 37
I. 1. revolting 2. intrude 3. outlook
   4. smuggling 5. starvation
II. 1. C 2. B 3. E 4. D 5. A

Level 6 Test 38
I. 1. dusk 2. publicized 3. exert
   4. underestimate 5. lessen
II. 1. E 2. B 3. D 4. C 5. A

Level 6 Test 39
I. 1. preach 2. puffed 3. flunked
   4. superficial 5. heroic
II. 1. B 2. D 3. E 4. C 5. A

Level 6 Test 40
I. 1. zoomed 2. snored 3. expiration
   4. tiptoe 5. punctual
II. 1. D 2. E 3. C 4. A 5. B

Intermediate Reading:
英文閱讀 High Five

掌握大考新趨勢，搶先練習新題型！

王隆興 編著

★全書分為 5 大主題：生態物種、人文歷史、科學科技、環境保育、醫學保健，共 50 篇由外籍作者精心編寫之文章。

★題目仿 111 學年度學測參考試卷命題方向設計，為未來大考提前作準備，搶先練習第二部分新題型——混合題。

★隨書附贈解析夾冊，方便練習後閱讀文章中譯及試題解析，並於解析補充每回文章精選的 15 個字彙。

20分鐘 稱霸 大考英文作文

王靖賢　編著

- 共16回作文練習，涵蓋大考作文3大題型：看圖寫作、主題寫作、信函寫作。根據近年大考趨勢精心出題，題型多元且擬真度高。
- 每回作文練習皆有為考生精選的英文名言佳句，增強考生備考戰力。
- 附方便攜帶的解析本，針對每回作文題目提供寫作架構圖，讓寫作脈絡一目了然，並提供範文、寫作要點、寫作撇步及好用詞彙，一本在手即可增強英文作文能力。